# ADRIFT IN SPACE

by Sally Odgers

illustrated by Matt Lin

SCH

D0416118

All rights reserved.
This 2009 edition published in the United Kingdom.by
Scholastic Ltd
Villiers House
Clarendon Avenue
Leamington Spa
Warwickshire
CV32 5PR

First published in 2007
by Macmillan Education Australia Pty Ltd.

Copyright © 2007 Laguna Bay Publishing Pty Ltd.
www.lagunabaypublishing.com

Text by Sally Odgers
Illustrations by Matt Lin
Cover Design Allison Parry
Design by Matt Lin/Goblin Design
Managing Editor Nicola Robinson

Out of this World: Adrift in Space
ISBN 978 1407 10179 8

Printed by Tien Wah Press, Singapore

1 2 3 4 5 6 7 8 9     9 0 1 2 3 4 5 6 7 8

S    P    A    C    E    S    P    O    R    T    S

# Contents

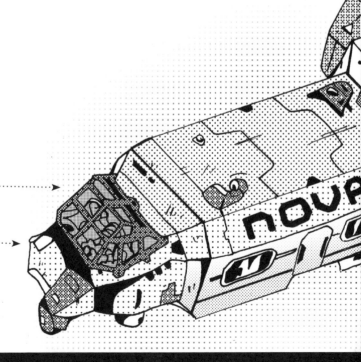

# Three kinds of people live on Space Station Nova.

The Stationborn have been there for generations.

The Prof

Luke

Coach

Janna

The Shipborn were born on giant spaceships that wander the Galaxy.

Pavros

The Earthborn came to Nova from Earth.

Ellie

There has always been rivalry between the three sets of Stationers but one thing brings them together: the game they call 3D.

- 11 -

- 13 -

- 20 -

# chapter 3 : Prof

- 27 -

- 33 -

- 34 -

WHAT DO YOU MEAN, TAKEN THE SKIPPER?

I— WHAT IS IT, PAV?

MAD K'S AWAKE.

YOU'LL PAY FOR THIS, KLIKWITZ!

BUT ... BUT ... BUT ...

SO ... THIS IS THE "LATEST DEEP SPACE TECHNOLOGY"?

OOHHH, MY HEAD ACHES.

THAT'S BECAUSE WE'RE RUNNING OUT OF AIR. YOUR GREEN-OX SYSTEM FILTER IS CLOGGED.

AIR CONTROL

MEANWHILE, ON BOARD THE STARTRADER FAIR DEAL ...

INCOMING VESSEL, CAPTAIN MERCHANT. HAILING HER ... NOW.

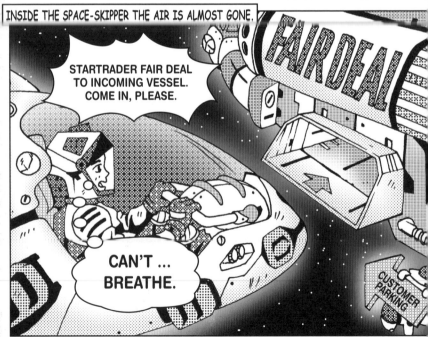

INSIDE THE SPACE-SKIPPER THE AIR IS ALMOST GONE.

STARTRADER FAIR DEAL TO INCOMING VESSEL. COME IN, PLEASE.

CAN'T ... BREATHE.

# chapter 5 : Fair Deal

THE SPACE-SKIPPER ARRIVES SAFELY ON THE FAIR DEAL.

DOCKING YOU NOW, TRADER.

UP ON THE FAIR DEAL'S BRIDGE THE CAPTAIN AND CREW WATCH LUKE'S LANDING ON SCREEN.

WHAT DO YOU MAKE OF THIS, COM?

NEVER SAW ANYTHING LIKE IT, CAP. HOW COULD A CRAFT SO SMALL SURVIVE OUT THERE?

OWWW, OOHHH.

EITHER WAY, WE NEED TO GET DOWN TO THE HANGAR AND FAST! THE FELLOW LOOKS TO BE IN TROUBLE!

YES, SIR!

- 43 -

HELLO THERE, MISS. CAPTAIN MERCHANT HERE. PLEASED TO MEET YOU.

THE COCKPIT IS STRAIGHT DOWN THERE.

PLEASE HURRY! WE'RE ALMOST OUT OF AIR!

THERE! I'LL JUST SWITCH INTO THE SYSTEM—

THERE!

SUDDENLY NOVA-K'S GRAVITY RETURNS.

UGH!

THUD!

UHH ... WHAT? WHO ARE YOU?

CAPTAIN MERCHANT, AND I JUST FIXED YOUR SHIP!

CAPTAIN MERCHANT EXITS THE COCKPIT TO TELL THE OTHERS ABOUT NOVA-K'S STATUS.

WELL, FOLKS, IT'S ALL FIXED! THE STABILIZER AND GREEN-OX IS NOW OPERATIONAL.

GOODBYE. HERE'S MY CARD ... MENTION MY NAME IF YOU NEED ADVERTISING, MY GOOD MAN.

MAYOR K

ER-HMMM.

- 45 -